For Marta and Huw

Published by Dbee Press
8 New Row, Mullingar, Co. Westmeath, Ireland
Text copyright © Dolores Keaveney 2015
Illustration copyright © Dolores Keaveney 2015
Artwork copyright © Dolores Keaveney 2015

Printed in Ireland by KPS Colour Print Ltd

Design & Layout by Gary Kelly

Written and Illustrated by Dolores Keaveney
www.doloreskeaveney.com

ISBN 978-0-9571917-6-1

The adventures of Hungry the chick

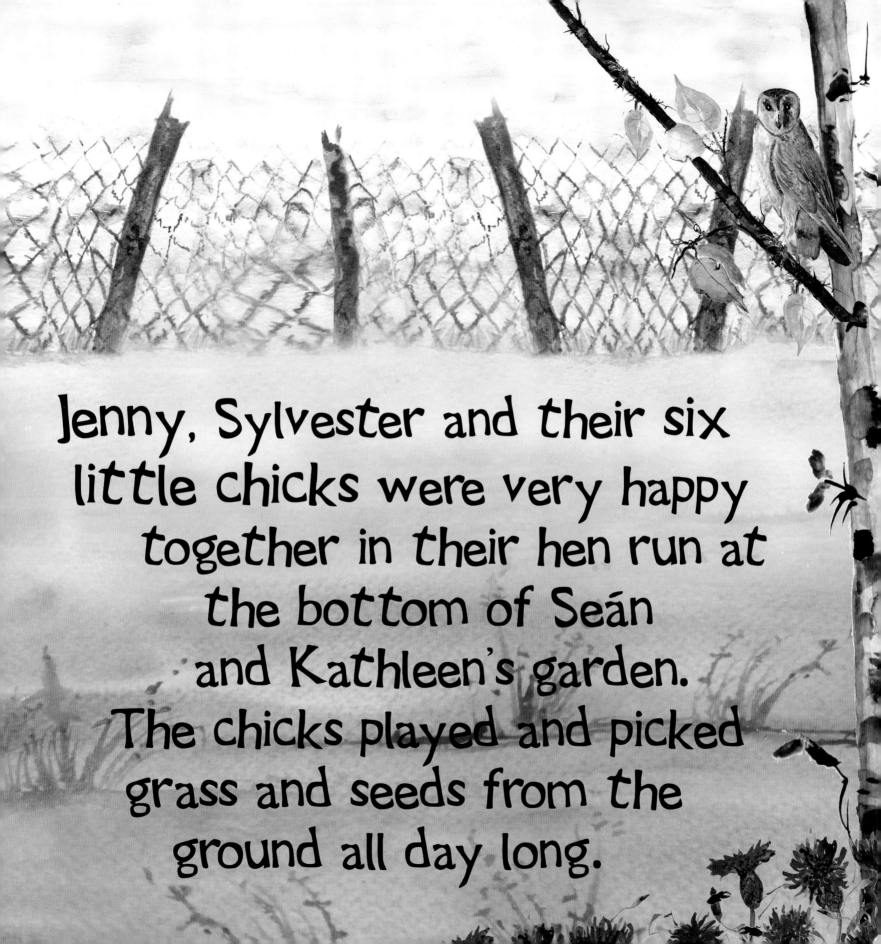

Jenny, Sylvester and their six little chicks were very happy together in their hen run at the bottom of Seán and Kathleen's garden. The chicks played and picked grass and seeds from the ground all day long.

No matter how many seeds and herbs Hungry the chick nibbled on in the hen run, he never felt full. "I am still very hungry and I need more food," he clucked. The other chicks were happy, but Hungry was not.

He could see a very big field nearby with lots of grass, herbs and seeds. "It would be great if I could get out and just run into that lovely field. I could fill my tummy and be back here before anybody misses me," thought Hungry to himself.

Hungry remembered when his father Sylvester, his mother Jenny and the other chicks went on their first adventure and how frightened they were when they got lost, but he decided that it was worth a try.

He went to the corner of the hen run. He scraped and scraped until he made the smallest hole, just big enough for him to creep out.

Off he went into the big field. It was beautiful, with lots of grass, herbs and seeds for him to pick. He was very happy.

Some COWS lived in the big field.

They soon came to see who the new arrival was.

Hungry looked up and *to his* amazement there was a very inquisitive cow looking at him closely. It lowered its head and spoke to Hungry. "My name is Betty," said the cow. "Who are you?"

"My name is Hungry and I am here to eat lots of seeds and grass. I am a very hungry little chick, you see, and there is not enough to eat in my hen run."

"You shouldn't be here," said Betty the cow. "It is very dangerous for a little chick like you to be in a big field on your own."

Hungry decided not to listen
to the cow and ran further
down the field. He picked
and picked on grass, herbs
and seeds until he was full.
He started to feel very tired.
"I will lie down here and have
a little rest," he thought.
He found a lovely soft
clump of grass and lay down.
Soon he was fast asleep.

Many hours passed. Suddenly Hungry awoke. He was frightened. He could see a scary fox looking at him. "Help! Help!" screamed Hungry. But the scary fox said "You are wasting your time screaming. Nobody can hear you! I am a hungry fox and you look like a very tasty little chick," he said.

Why not go
and catch something bigger?"
Hungry was terrified
and knew that
he was in great
danger.

He pushed himself deeper into
the big clump of grass
and hid there until the
next day. The scary
fox crept around all
night, waiting for the
little chick to come out.

In the morning, Hungry poked his head out of the clump of grass. The fox was just about to pounce on the little chick, when Sean came to the rescue just in the nick of time.

He had been looking for Hungry everywhere and was delighted to find him. The scary fox ran away as fast as he could.

"Come here you naughty little chick!" said Sean. "You are very lucky indeed that I found you." Sean picked Hungry up and took him back to the hen run.

Sylvester, Jenny and the other chicks were delighted to see Hungry again. They were sure that he was gone forever!

Hungry was so happy to be back home and he promised he would never leave the family again. I wonder, will he keep his promise?